恼人的水痘

【美】琳达·威廉姆斯·亚伯◎著

【美】吉奥雅·法蒙吉◎绘

范晓星◎译

天津出版传媒集团

新蕾出版社

献给我的表妹：苏菲、克洛伊和麦迪逊。

——琳达·威廉姆斯·亚伯

图书在版编目 (CIP) 数据

恼人的水痘/(美)亚伯(Aber,L.W.)著;(美)
法蒙吉(Fiammenghi,G.)绘;范晓星译.—天津:新
蕾出版社,2015.5(2024.12重印)
(数学帮帮忙·互动版)
书名原文：Who's Got Spots?
ISBN 978-7-5307-6221-9

Ⅰ.①恼… Ⅱ.①亚…②法…③范… Ⅲ.①数学–
儿童读物 Ⅳ.①01-49

中国版本图书馆 CIP 数据核字(2015)第 074448 号

Who's Got Spots? by Linda Williams Aber;
Illustrated by Gioia Fiammenghi.

Copyright © 2000 by Kane Press, Inc.

All rights reserved, including the right of reproduction in whole or in part in any
form. This edition published by arrangement with Kane Press, Inc. New York, NY,
represented by Lerner Publishing Group through The ChoiceMaker Korea Co.
agency.

Simplified Chinese translation copyright © 2015 by New Buds Publishing House
(Tianjin) Limited Company

ALL RIGHTS RESERVED

本书中文简体版专有出版权经由中华版权代理中心授予新蕾出版社(天津)有
限公司。未经许可,不得以任何方式复制或抄袭本书的任何部分。

津图登字：02-2012-238

出版发行：天津出版传媒集团
　　　　　新蕾出版社

http://www.newbuds.com.cn

地　　址：天津市和平区西康路 35 号(300051)
出 版 人：马玉秀
电　　话：总编办(022)23332422
　　　　　发行部(022)23332679　23332351
传　　真：(022)23332422
经　　销：全国新华书店
印　　刷：天津新华印务有限公司
开　　本：787mm×1092mm　1/16
印　　张：3
版　　次：2015 年 5 月第 1 版　2024 年 12 月第 21 次印刷
定　　价：12.00 元

无处不在的数学

资深编辑　卢　江

　　人们常说"兴趣是最好的老师"，有了兴趣，学习就会变得轻松愉快。数学对于孩子来说或许有些难，因为比起语文，数学显得枯燥、抽象，不容易理解，孩子往往不那么喜欢。可许多家长都知道，学数学对于孩子的成长和今后的生活有多么重要。不仅数学知识很有用，学习数学过程中获得的数学思想和方法更会影响孩子的一生，因为数学素养是构成人基本素质的一个重要因素。但是，怎样才能让孩子对数学产生兴趣呢？怎样才能激发他们兴致勃勃地去探索数学问题呢？我认为，让孩子读些有趣的书或许是不错的选择。读了这套"数学帮帮忙"，我立刻产生了想把它们推荐给教师和家长朋友们的愿望，因为这真是一套会让孩子爱上数学的好书！

　　这套有趣的图书从美国引进，原出版者是美国资深教育专家。每本书讲述一个孩子们生活中的故事，由故事中出现的问题自然地引入一个数学知识，然后通过运用数学知识解决问题。比如，从帮助外婆整理散落的纽扣引出分类，从为小狗记录藏骨头的地点引出空间方位等等。故事素材全

部来源于孩子们的真实生活，不是童话，不是幻想，而是鲜活的生活实例。正是这些发生在孩子身边的故事，让孩子们懂得，数学无处不在并且非常有用；这些鲜活的实例也使得抽象的概念更易于理解，更容易激发孩子学习数学的兴趣，让他们逐渐爱上数学。这样的教育思想和方法与我国近年来提倡的数学教育理念是十分吻合的！

这是一套适合5~8岁孩子阅读的书，书中的有趣情节和生动的插画可以将抽象的数学问题直观化、形象化，为孩子的思维活动提供具体形象的支持。如果亲子共读的话，家长可以带领孩子推测情节的发展，探讨解决难题的办法，让孩子在愉悦的氛围中学到知识和方法。

值得教师和家长朋友们注意的是，在每本书的后面，出版者还加入了"互动课堂"及"互动练习"，一方面通过一些精心设计的活动让孩子巩固新学到的数学知识，进一步体会知识的含义和实际应用；另一方面帮助家长指导孩子阅读，体会故事中数学之外的道理，逐步提升孩子的阅读理解能力。

我相信孩子读过这套书后一定会明白，原来，数学不是烦恼，不是包袱，数学真能帮大忙！

"祝你好运！"齐普的爸爸喊道。

今天是贝克老师宣布秋季音乐节独唱人选的日子。齐普希望那个人就是他！

3

齐普坐立不安。他太兴奋了，也有些担心。如果贝克老师站在全班同学面前说出别人的名字怎么办？要是她说的名字是……

"齐普！"贝克老师笑着宣布，"齐普同学将是我们的独唱歌手！"

　　全班同学都热烈欢呼。从试唱以来，齐普第一次放轻松了。今天是多么美好的一天啊！

排练马上开始了。"我们需要很多人声来完成合唱。"贝克老师说,"齐普负责独唱的部分。但你们每个人都非常重要。所以,每次排练都一定要来。"

"放心吧!"齐普说道。他非常肯定没有什么会影响到他们的演出。

可是第二天，齐普就发现麻烦来了……

"我有个坏消息。"贝克老师说,"合唱队有3位同学出水痘了,他们是:特拉维斯、麦伊和科里。"

　　孩子们马上七嘴八舌地议论起来:

　　"你得过水痘吗?"

　　"我早就得过了。"

　　"我会不会传染上呀?"

　　"你是怎么得的水痘?"

　　……

贝克老师说:"你可能会从得水痘的人那里传染上水痘。但好消息是,一旦你得过水痘,就再也不会得了。"

可同学们还是很担心,议论纷纷。

　　"那咱们的演出怎么办？"齐普问。

　　"嗯，我们来想想看。"贝克老师说，"我们合唱队一共有 15 位同学。只要有 10 位同学在演出时不生病，我们就可以表演了。"

"这可能性有多大？"和齐普坐同桌的女孩艾丽丝小声说，"水痘传染性很强呢！"

　　"我知道。"齐普忧心忡忡地说。

　　贝克老师叹了口气："咱们只能等等看，谁知道接下来的两周会发生什么呢？"

　　"等待消除不了咱们的担心。"放学回家的路上，齐普对艾丽丝说，"我希望自己能弄明白，在演出当天我们有 10 个同学不生病的可能性有多大。"

　　"哈哈！"艾丽丝笑着说，"你有水晶球吗？能预测谁会出水痘吗？"

齐普露出了笑容。"回头跟你说。"他说,"现在我要回家去做一件事,准比水晶球还灵! 我要做一张图表!"

齐普心想，有 3 个同学正在出水痘，这只会持续 7 到 10 天，所以他们到时正好参加演出。他在"正在出水痘"这一栏里，画了三个记号。然后，又在"从未得过"这一栏里画了一个记号。这个记号代表他自己。

　　齐普看看图表，"已经得过"这一栏目前为止还是空的。

　　"要给 11 个同学打电话！"他说，"最好现在就打！"

　　齐普最先给艾丽丝打电话。"我在调查出水痘的情况。"他告诉艾丽丝，"你出过水痘吗？"

　　"我去年出过了。"艾丽丝说，"因为我不能出门，还是你替我去要的万圣节糖果呢，记得吗？"

　　"对呀！"齐普说完，在图表上画上一个记号。

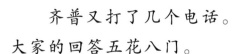

齐普又打了几个电话。
大家的回答五花八门。

"我出过。"吉姆说,"那
时我正在参加夏令营,我就
一直挠啊挠啊!"

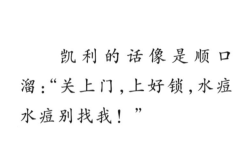

凯利的话像是顺口
溜:"关上门,上好锁,水痘
水痘别找我!"

16

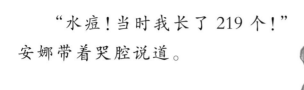

"水痘！当时我长了 219 个！"
安娜带着哭腔说道。

"我妈非让我戴手套，这
样我就不会把水痘抓破了。"
马特告诉齐普。

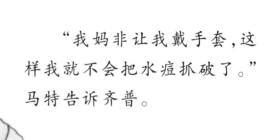

齐普又给苏菲和克洛伊打
电话，她们两个都没出过水痘。
在"从未出过"这一栏加两个，
还剩下最后四个电话，他想。

第二天，齐普向全班展示他的图表。"大家请看，"他解释道，"我们有7位同学可以参加演出。"

"你怎么知道的？"罗伯问。

"是这样的，"齐普说，"有4位同学已经得过水痘，所以他们不会再得了。3位正在出水痘的同学还有足够的时间好起来，他们也能参加演出。这是7位同学。我们总共需要10个人。"

“我懂了。”艾米说，“所以我们当中至少有3个人要保持健康！”

从那一刻开始，每个没有得过水痘的同学都千方百计让自己不要传染上。

艾米戴上了从医生那里要来的口罩。"别对着我呼吸！"她对每个人都这么说。

弗雷德一天到晚都戴着手套！"每天戴手套，病毒全没招！"他说。

杰克逊给教室里的椅子全喷上了除菌灵。"一定
要万无一失！"他低声说着。

齐普则努力尝试闭着嘴唱歌！"这样做是为了保
护我的嗓子。"他呜呜噜噜地说。

第二天，克洛伊、弗雷德和苏菲没来。"他们得水痘了。"贝克老师难过地说，"不过，特拉维斯、麦伊和科里明天就回来了。"

"哎哟！"齐普说，"我的图表不灵了，我没法跟进谁得病，谁没得病。"

"我们再做一张带人名的图表怎么样？"艾丽丝提议道，"用便利贴就可以。"

"好主意！"齐普说，"我们可以根据情况变化调整人名的位置。"

　　"好了!"当他们做好图表时,齐普说,"离演出还有两天。如果其他人不再生病的话,我们会有12位同学。"

　　演出前一天，贝克老师带来了更糟的消息。"凯利和杰克逊也出水痘了！"她边说边摇着头。

"哦,不!我们减到 10 个人了!"齐普转身对罗伯和艾米说,"你们俩听好,咱们谁都不能生病了!"

25

那天晚上，齐普发现一件非常可怕的事！他脱衬衫时看了眼肚皮，不由得大惊失色："哦，不！我也出水痘了！"

齐普真想哭。他暗自想，我一定要参加演出！我跟谁也不说。

齐普爬进被窝。屋子里漆黑一片，他想的全是独唱的事，再也高兴不起来了，他心知肚明这是为什么。

　　齐普坐起来大喊："妈妈！爸爸！我出水痘了！"

　　爸爸妈妈冲进卧室，打开了灯。齐普给他们看身上那个红点。爸爸细细打量完大笑起来："你不是出水痘，那只是一颗痣。"

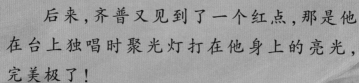

后来,齐普又见到了一个红点,那是他
在台上独唱时聚光灯打在他身上的亮光,
完美极了!

30

数 据 图 表

艾米和弗雷德做了一项调查,他们问了很多同学这个问题:

下次演出时,你愿意担任独唱吗?

然后,他们把收集到的数据整理成这样的图表:

请用以上图表来说明下面的话是否正确。

1. 艾米和弗雷德总共调查了 11 名同学。

2. 愿意独唱的同学比不愿意的多。

3. 罗伯不愿意独唱。

4. 克洛伊也许愿意独唱。

5. 下次演出可能有 8 位同学愿意独唱。

互动课堂

亲爱的家长朋友，请您和孩子一起完成下面这些内容，会有更大的收获哟！

提高阅读能力

• 只看封面和书名，让孩子猜猜这本书讲的是一个什么故事。

• 看完第 8 页，给孩子讲讲水痘这种疾病。参照第 9 页上的内容，让孩子明白出水痘到底是怎么一回事。

• 用第 12~13 页的插图锻炼孩子的读图能力。请孩子判断图中是什么季节，并说出他是从哪里看出来的。

• 读完故事，请孩子想一想，齐普决定告诉爸爸妈妈自己得了水痘，为什么这样做是正确的？如果他不说，会有什么后果呢？

巩固数学概念

- 给孩子讲一讲"独唱"这个词的含义。如果齐普和另外一个孩子一起唱,那就叫"二重唱",那什么是"三重唱"、"四重唱"呢?

- 和孩子一起检查故事里的计算是否正确。比如第 10 页,老师说合唱队有 15 个人。在第 15 页,齐普知道有 3 个孩子已经出过水痘,所以他要给 11 个人打电话。让孩子把这些人数加起来,说一说第 15 个人在哪儿?

- 在人数统计表上,每 5 个人一组,这种计数方法既简单又快捷。试着让孩子 5 个 5 个地数数。

- 根据第 15~17 页齐普电话调查的结果,请孩子想一想,用第 32 页上的哪个图表更容易看出有多少同学出过水痘?

生活中的数学

- 请孩子自己调查一下,他的房间里有多少种玩具?每种玩具有几个?好朋友们最喜欢的颜色是什么?帮孩子整理好收集来的数据,并制成图表。

- 请孩子留意报纸、杂志和产品说明书中的图表,和孩子聊一聊,这些图表的内容是什么? 它们又是怎样展示数据的?

选什么颜色?

要过圣诞节啦,我们要把场景布置成什么颜色好呢?大家都来说说看!

艾丽丝说:"我喜欢红色。"
罗伯说:"不,我觉得蓝色好!"
科里说:"黄色的不错!"
克洛伊说:"我也喜欢黄的。"
马特:"圣诞节配蓝色最合适!"
凯利:"我同意马特的想法。"
杰克逊:"嗯,蓝色的挺好!"

那就少数服从多数吧!

颜色统计		
红色	蓝色	黄色

大家最后选的颜色是 _____。

快来帮帮我

我要开始喽：艾丽丝跳舞，罗伯唱歌，科里演话剧，克洛伊也演话剧，马特唱歌，凯利跳舞，杰克逊跳舞。

爸爸妈妈，我们要过圣诞节啦，每位同学都报了一项节目，老师让我帮她整理一下，你们帮我念念吧！

亲爱的，你可要记清楚哟：麦伊唱歌，吉姆、安娜和特拉维斯演话剧，马可唱歌。好了，就这些，你都记下了吗？

你们看,老师一定喜欢我做的图表,我多聪明呀!

圣诞节目报名表

唱 歌	跳 舞	演话剧

孩子,真不错!记录好每个节目报名的人后,你就可以把人数也列出来,那样更清楚,你会做吗?

圣诞节目报名人数表

唱 歌	跳 舞	演话剧

宝贝,你做得很棒,通过这两个图表,你可以告诉老师,_____ 的报名人数最多,_____ 的报名人数最少。如果是一台完整的节目,还应该有一位主持人哟!

37

数一数

圣诞节晚会上,数量最多的花瓶要放到主席台上,数量最少的要当作奖品,帮我数一数吧!

我们的圣诞树

现在我知道了，_____ 最多，
_____ 最少，它们相差 _____ 个。

哪个节目最精彩？

A

舞 蹈	歌 曲	话 剧
/////// //////	/////// //////	///////

B

舞 蹈	歌 曲	话 剧
∨∨∨∨∨∨∨ ∨∨∨∨∨	∨∨∨∨∨∨∨∨ ∨∨∨∨∨∨∨	∨∨∨∨∨∨∨∨

C

舞 蹈	歌 曲	话 剧
正正一	正正正	正丁

我最喜欢写"正"字计数，因为一个"正"字刚好有 5 画。

现在你知道哪个节目最精彩了吗？你觉得三位同学做的图表，哪一个更便于统计呢？

试一试

请你用喜欢的符号来统计一下吧！

天气				
符号				
天数				

互动练习1

颜色统计		
红色	蓝色	黄色
✓	✓✓✓✓	✓✓

蓝色

互动练习2

圣诞节目报名表		
唱 歌	跳 舞	演话剧
罗伯　马特 麦伊　马可	艾丽丝 凯利 杰克逊	科里　克洛伊 吉姆　安娜 特拉维斯

圣诞节目报名人数表		
唱 歌	跳 舞	演话剧
4	3	5

演话剧　跳舞

互动练习3

4	6	3

互动练习4

7	10	3	8

圆球　靴子　7

互动练习5 歌曲

互动练习6

天气				
天数	14	12	2	3

（习题设计:董惠平　骆　双）

Who's Got Spots?

"Good luck!" called Kip's dad.

This was the day Ms. Beck was going to announce the solo singer for the Autumn Fest. Kip was hoping it would be him.

Kip could hardly sit still. He was too excited. He was also worried. What if Ms. Beck stood up in front of the whole class and said someone else's name?

What if the name she called was...

"Kip!" Ms. Beck announced with a big smile. "Kip will be our solo singer!"

All the kids cheered. For the first time since tryouts, Kip relaxed. What a great day this was turning out to be!

Practice for the Autumn Fest began right away. "It takes many voices to make a chorus," said Ms. Beck. "Kip will sing the solo, but each one of you is important. So be sure to come to every practice."

"Don't worry," said Kip. He was sure that nothing would get in the way of their show.

But the next day Kip found out that something was getting in the way...

"I have bad news," said Ms. Beck. "Three people in the chorus have chicken pox—Travis, Mai and Cory."

All the kids began talking at once. "Have you had it?...I've had it already...Will I get it?...How did you get chicken pox?"

Ms. Beck said, "You catch it from someone who has it. The good news is that once you get chicken pox, you can never get it again."

Still, the room buzzed with worried voices.

"What about the show?"cried Kip.

"Well, let's see,"Ms. Beck said."There are fifteen people in our chorus. We can perform if at least ten are well by the date of the show."

"What are the chances of that?"whispered Alice, the girl next to Kip. "Chicken pox is really contagious!"

"I know,"said Kip in a worried voice.

Ms. Beck sighed,"All we can do is wait and see. Who knows what will happen in the next two weeks?"

"Waiting won't take the worry away,"Kip said to Alice on the way home from school. "I wish I could figure out what the chances are for ten of us to be well on the day of the show."

"Ha!"Alice laughed."Do you have a crystal ball that tells about chicken pox?"

A smile spread across Kip's face."I'll talk to you later,"he said. "I'm going home now to make something that will tell us more than a crystal ball. I'm going to make a chart!"

Kip thought, "Three kids have chicken pox now. It only lasts 7 to 10 days. So they'll be better in time for the show."He made three marks in the HAVE IT NOW column. Then he made one mark under NEVER HAD IT. That mark was for himself.

Kip looked at the chart. The HAD IT column didn't have any marks yet.

"Eleven kids to call!"he said."Better get started!"

Kip called Alice first. "I'm doing a chicken pox survey,"he told her. "Have you had chicken pox?"

"I had chicken pox last year,"Alice said."You went trick-or-treating for me because I couldn't go out, remember?"

"That's right!"Kip said. He marked his chart.

Kip made more calls. Everyone had something different to say.

"I had it,"Jim said. "I was scratching the whole time I was away at camp!"

"I'll shut the doors and turn the locks. I'll never get the chicken pox! " rhymed Kelly.

"Chicken pox! I had 219 spots!"wailed Anna.

"My mom made me wear mittens so I wouldn't scratch,"Matt told him.

Kip called Sophie and Chloe next. Neither of them had had chicken pox. "Two more in the NEVER HAD IT column. Only four more calls to make," he thought.

The next day Kip showed the chart to the class. "Look,"he said. "We have seven kids for the show."

"How do you figure that?"asked Rob.

"Like this,"explained Kip. "Four kids had chicken pox already, so they can't get it again. The three kids who have it now should be better in plenty of time to sing. That's seven kids. All we need is ten."

"I get it,"said Amy."So at least three more of us have to stay healthy!"

From that second on, everyone who had never had chicken pox tried everything NOT to get chicken pox.

Amy started wearing a mask she got from a doctor's office. "Don't breathe on me!"she said to everyone.

Fred wore gloves all day! "A glove a day keeps the germs away!"he said.

Jackson sprayed germ-killer on the chairs in the classroom. "Just to be extra safe,"he whispered.

And Kip tried very hard to sing with his mouth closed! "To protect my throat,"he mumbled.

The next day Chloe, Fred and Sophie were absent. "Chicken pox," Ms. Beck said sadly."But Travis, Mai and Cory will be back tomorrow."

"Uh, oh,"said Kip."My chart doesn't work so well anymore. I can't keep track of who's sick and who isn't."

"How about making a graph with the kids' names on it?"Alice suggested."We can use sticky notes."

"Great idea!"said Kip. "Then we can move them around if things change."

"Whew! "Kip said when they were finished. "It's two days till the show. If nobody else gets sick, we'll have twelve kids."

The day before the show Ms. Beck had some more bad news. "Kelly and Jackson,"she said, shaking her head."Chicken pox!"

"Oh, no!"Kip thought. "We're down to ten!"He turned to Rob and Amy."Okay, you guys. None of us can get sick!"

That night Kip made a terrible discovery. When he took off his shirt, he looked at his stomach and gasped."Oh, no! I've got a spot!"

Kip felt like crying. He thought,"I have to be in the show! I just won't tell anyone."

Kip crawled under the covers. In the darkness he thought about his solo. He didn't feel good about it anymore. And he knew why.

Kip sat up and shouted,"Mom, Dad! I have chicken pox!"

His parents hurried into his room and turned on the light. Kip showed them the spot. Dad looked closely, and then he laughed. "You don't have chicken pox,"he said."That spot's just a freckle!"

And the next spot Kip saw was the spotlight shining on him as he sang his solo—perfectly!